D0003154

CONTENTS

IN RECOGNITION

These staff members of The Navigators made the major contribution to the prayerful and thoughtful preparation of *God's Design for the Family:* Rod Beidler, Bruce Das, Ray Hoo, Doug Prensner, Ed Reis, Gene Soderberg, and Bob Sparks. The aim of the series has been to provide married couples with biblical principles and patterns that lead to dynamic family growth in love, and to harmony in their relationships with God and their families.

In addition, appreciation is due to the wives of the staff members, who provided help and ideas as the project developed; to other Navigator staff members who participated in various stages of planning and preparing the series; and to a large number of staff, pastors, and lay men and women who field-tested the manuscripts.

BEFORE YOU BEGIN

These studies are written for use by married couples, or by singles planning to be married. Both partners should answer the questions separately, and then discuss them with each other. You will gain even more benefit by meeting regularly with other couples after all of you have answered the questions. The recommended pace is one chapter per week, with a group discussion time for each chapter. Group discussion guidelines for all the chapters are included in this book, beginning on page 83.

Each chapter includes application questions and family project ideas to help you apply to your family life the things you are learning in your study. Before deciding on each application, remember to pray about it. God knows the needs in your life which He wants you to work on now. Stay in communication with Him as you plan, and be confident that He will lead you. Pray also for insight and strength in putting your applications into practice.

CHAPTER 1

UNDERSTANDING GOD'S CREATION

WHERE did I come from? What determined who I am? What is the purpose of my life? Whose idea is marriage and the family?

What we believe about these questions significantly affects our attitudes toward life and other people—particularly our families. Thankfully, the Scriptures point us to the right answers.

OUR CREATOR

1. Summarize in your own words what the following passages teach about God and the origin of all things.

Genesis 1:1-2 _____

_____

_____

John 1:1-3 _____

_____

_____

Acts 17:24-28 _____

_____

_____

What title would you give to God that would summarize what you observed in these passages?

_____

2. Read carefully Isaiah 40:10-29, and write down
   four or five things you observe in this passage
   about God.

   _____

   _____

   _____

   _____

   _____

   _____

   _____

   _____

   _____

   _____

   _____

3. What do the following passages reveal about God?

   Job 12:13 _____

   _____

   _____

   Psalm 147:5 _____

   _____

   _____

   Jeremiah 10:7 _____

   _____

   _____

Romans 16:27 _____

_____

_____

1 Corinthians 1:25 _____

_____

_____

How would you summarize the teaching of these passages?

_____

_____

_____

_____

_____

GOD'S DESIGN IN CREATION

4. Review Genesis 1:1—2:3, and list the things God created or established.

_____

_____

_____

_____

_____

_____

_____

_____

_____

5. How did God view what He had created? (Genesis 1:31)

_____

_____

6. What do these passages say about God's work?

Deuteronomy 32:4 _____

_____

_____

Psalm 104:24 _____

_____

_____

Proverbs 3:19 _____

_____

_____

7. Paul described the position of Jesus Christ in God's creation in Colossians 1:15-20. From this passage, how would you describe Christ's position?

_____

_____

_____

_____

_____

"All God's acts are done in perfect wisdom, first for His own glory, and then for the highest good of the greatest number for the longest time. And all His acts are as pure as they are wise, and as good as they are wise and pure."

—A. W. Tozer*

*A.W. Tozer, _Knowledge of the Holy_ (New York: Harper and Row Publishers, 1961), page 66.

SEEING OURSELVES AS GOD SEES US

8. Consider Genesis 1:27 and 5:1. What do you think it means that God created man and woman "in His own image" and "in the likeness of God"?

_____

_____

_____

_____

9. Summarize what David wrote about himself in Psalm 139:13-16.

_____

_____

_____

_____

10. What did Paul write about himself in 1 Corinthians 15:10?

_____

_____

11. What did Paul write about God's purpose for us in the following passages?

1 Corinthians 6:19-20 _____

_____

_____

1 Corinthians 10:31 _____

_____

_____

12. List some ways you believe we can bring honor and glory to God in our families.

_____

_____

_____

_____

_____

_____

13. What do you see in the following passages about how the Lord regards us?

Galatians 4:4-6 _____

_____

_____

John 10:27-29 _____

_____

_____

John 15:13-15 _____

_____

_____

_____

1 Timothy 2:3-4 _____

_____

_____

GOD'S DESIGN FOR THE FAMILY

14. From Genesis 1:26-28 and 2:18-24, how would you describe God's purpose for the family?

14

_____

_____

_____

_____

_____

15. What responsibilities were given to parents in
Deuteronomy 6:4-9 and Psalm 78:5-8?

_____

_____

_____

16. Read the verses below. In what ways does the
family illustrate God's relationship to us?

Psalm 103:13 _____

_____

_____

Matthew 7:11 _____

_____

_____

Hebrews 12:7-10 _____

_____

_____

17. Read Mark 10:2-9 and Malachi 2:15-16. What does
God say about how long a marriage relationship
should last?

_____

_____

_____

_____

15

> "The family belongs to God. He created it. He determined its inner structure. He appointed for it its purpose and goal."
>
> —Larry Christenson*

APPLICATION

(In the application section at the end of each chapter you may find it helpful to discuss what you have written with your spouse, and perhaps with others in your family.)

18. Write a brief statement of what you believe are the most important things you learned in this chapter about God and His design.

_____

_____

_____

_____

19. Select one or two passages from this chapter which particularly impressed you. List their references, and write down the thoughts from each passage which impressed you. Consider memorizing the verse or verses you selected.

_____

_____

_____

_____

_____

20. After prayerfully reviewing your answers in this chapter, do you know of any need in your life that

*Larry Christenson, *The Christian Family* (Minneapolis: Bethany Fellowship, 1970), page 11.

you should work on at this time? If so, briefly describe this need.

_____

_____

_____

What passage of Scripture brought this to your attention?

_____

_____

_____

What specific action will you take to meet this need?

_____

_____

_____

How will you evaluate your progress?

_____

_____

FAMILY PROJECTS

(Choose one or more projects each week. These projects and those listed at the end of later chapters can be a valuable exercise for practicing the scriptural principles you have studied. As you read the instructions, think of creative ways to make them meaningful and enjoyable for each member of your family. Plan to include every child who is old enough to enjoy the time with you. If your children are older, allow time for deeper discussion of thoughts and questions they may have, and let them help you plan the project.)

a. Read Psalm 100 together. Then discuss the psalm
for a few minutes by asking investigative questions beginning with who, what, where, when,
why, or how. For example:
   What should we know about the Lord?
   What does it mean that we are the sheep of
      His pasture?
   Why should we praise and thank God?
   What are we told to do?
Let each family member make up at least one
question to ask the others. After a time of
sharing, pray together. Let each person think of
something for which to thank God. You could encourage each one to thank God for creating him as
a unique person, and for loving and accepting him.

b. This week have each family member collect and
cut out pictures from magazines and newspapers
which depict his unique characteristics—and then
compile all the pictures into a family collage.
Discuss with each other how God has given you individual qualities which complement each other
and contribute to the unity of the family.

CHAPTER 2

RESPONDING TO GOD'S LOVE

FAR from being an impersonal force reigning over the universe with no interest in human beings, God is a loving God who has communicated to us His intense concern for every individual. Therefore we can be assured that He is personally interested in every member of our family, and wants each one to develop a relationship with Him. How should we respond to His great love? God tells us how.

WHAT IS GOD LIKE?

1. Read Exodus 3:13-14. What does God call Himself in this passage?

   _____

   What does this name suggest to you about God's nature?

   _____

   _____

   _____

   _____

2. What personality characteristics do you observe about God in the passages on the next page?

19

Numbers 11:1 _____

_____

_____

2 Chronicles 16:9 _____

_____

_____

Psalm 65:5 _____

_____

_____

Psalm 147:11 _____

_____

_____

Isaiah 14:27 _____

_____

_____

Jeremiah 31:3 _____

_____

_____

3. From Exodus 33:11 and Deuteronomy 34:10, describe the relationship God had with Moses.

_____

_____

_____

4. What did James write about Abraham's relationship with God (James 2:23)?

_____

_____

_____

5. Read 1 Thessalonians 1:9 and Psalm 115:2-7.
   What do these passages say about what God is
   like—and what He is not like?

   _____

   _____

   _____

6. Read 1 John 4:7-10. John wrote that love comes
   from God (verse 7) and that "God is love"
   (verse 8). What do these statements mean to you?

   _____

   _____

   _____

   _____

   _____

   _____

   _____

   > "Personality in God is difficult for the human mind
   > to grasp. But the Bible is insistent on this point,
   > and the elements of personality—mind, emotions (in
   > a sense differing from human emotions), will,
   > freedom—are attributed to Him. It is as *Spirit*
   > that He is Personal without any of the limiting
   > notions attached to our view of human personality."
   > —T. C. Hammond*

GOD LOVES US

7. List on the following page what you conclude
   about God's interest in people and His interest in
   you as an individual from John 3:16.

*T. C. Hammond, *In Understanding Be Men* (London: Inter-Varsity
Fellowship, 1936), page 51.

_____

_____

_____

_____

8. Read John 4:19-26. Write in your own words what Jesus said in verses 23 and 24.

_____

_____

_____

_____

_____

9. Identify from the following Scriptures what the Lord has done to reveal Himself to us.

Psalm 19:1-2 _____

_____

_____

Luke 24:27 _____

_____

_____

John 1:1, 1:14, and 1:18 _____

_____

_____

_____

John 16:5-11 _____

_____

_____

_____

Romans 1:18-20 _____

_____

_____

_____

Hebrews 1:1-2 _____

_____

_____

_____

10. Since we have experienced God's love personally, we should naturally look for ways to express our love for Him. In Mark 12:29-31 Jesus stated the most important commandments. Write these two commandments in your own words.

_____

_____

_____

_____

_____

_____

_____

_____

_____

11. What keeps people from having a personal relationship with God? (Read Isaiah 59:1-2 and Romans 3:23.)

_____

_____

Why is this true? (You may want to refer to
Romans 2:1-16.)

_____

_____

_____

_____

_____

12. From the following verses, tell what God has done
so we can have a personal relationship with Him.

Romans 5:8 _____

_____

_____

Romans 6:23 _____

_____

_____

1 Peter 3:18 _____

_____

_____

RESPONDING TO GOD'S LOVE

13. Read John 17:3. How did Jesus Christ define eternal life in this prayer?

_____

_____

14. From these passages, explain the first steps we
must take to know God personally: John 1:12,
3:16, and 5:24.

_____

_____

_____

_____

_____

_____

_____

_____

15. Jesus spoke to Nicodemus about the need to be "born again" (John 3:3). What does this mean to you?

_____

_____

_____

_____

(The illustration on pages 79-82 can help you understand more clearly the answers to Questions 13-15.)

EXPERIENCING GOD'S LOVE

16. Read John 14:21-23. What did Jesus say about the requirements for experiencing God's love and presence?

_____

_____

_____

_____

17. From Psalm 116:1-2 and 1 Peter 5:7, how else may we develop our relationship with God and experience His love?

_____

_____

_____

18. What do you observe in these passages from the examples of David, Daniel, and Jesus that can help us know God better?

David (Psalm 5:3)_____

_____

_____

Daniel (Daniel 6:10)_____

_____

_____

Jesus (Luke 5:15-16)_____

_____

_____

Good communication is essential to the development of any relationship, and is indispensable in our relationship with God. God longs to share His thoughts with us and to listen to us—to be involved with us.

Develop the daily habit of spending time alone with God. Here is a simple plan:

DAILY QUIET TIME
1. Set a definite time of day when you are most alert, and a specific length of time (start with seven to ten minutes).
2. Find a quiet place with few distractions.
3. Have your Bible, a notebook, and a pen with you.
4. Begin with prayer. You may want to use

Psalm 119:18 as your request: "Open my eyes that I may see wonderful things in Your law."

5. Meditate on a portion of Scripture as you read, study, or memorize it. Ask yourself two questions: What have I learned about God today? What does God want me to do today? Write down your answers.

6. Close with prayer. Remembering these four steps ("ACTS") may help you as you pray:

A (Adoration)—Praise God for what you learn or remember about Him.

C (Confession)—Confess any sin which God brings to your attention.

T (Thanksgiving)—Thank God specifically for the help He has given you.

S (Supplication)—Ask for God's help in meeting your specific needs and the needs of others.

19. Read the commands in Deuteronomy 11:18-21. What are one or two activities your family can use to develop their relationships with God?

_____

_____

_____

_____

Two excellent times for a family fellowship with God are bedtimes (with young children) and after dinner. Keep the time interesting, brief, practical, and centered on the Word—the living Word (Christ) and the written Word (the Bible).

APPLICATION

20. Based on what you have learned in this chapter, write a brief statement on the next page expressing what you believe about God's love.

_____

_____

_____

_____

21. Select one or two passages from this chapter
    which particularly impressed you. List the
    references, and write down the thoughts from
    each passage which impressed you. Then begin
    memorizing one or both verses.

_____

_____

_____

_____

_____

22. In view of what you have learned in this chapter,
    answer these questions:

    Do you have God's gift of eternal life?

    _____

    Are you now experiencing His love?

    _____

    Can you give examples of how you are experienc-
    ing His love?

    _____

    _____

    Is every member of your family experiencing a
    personal relationship with God?   ·

    _____

    If so, in what ways?

28

_____

_____

_____

_____

23. Prayerfully review your answers in this chapter,
and describe any needs you might want to work
on.

_____

_____

_____

_____

What one specific action will you take to meet one
of these needs?

_____

_____

_____

_____

How will you evaluate your progress?

_____

_____

FAMILY PROJECTS

(Choose one or more.)

a. Read together one of these passages, and then
discuss it using the questions on the next page or
some of your own.

Psalm 91
Psalm 112
Isaiah 40:30-31
Acts 22:6-15

29

Suggested discussion questions:

What is the main teaching in this passage?
What are some things that result when we know
   God personally?
What is it about God that first caused you to re-
   spond to Him in faith?
What is it about God that more than anything else
   continues to draw you to Him?

b. Make a family journal to record daily expressions
   of God's love to your family. Encourage each
   family member to write in his name, the date, and
   an example of how God has shown His love, and
   how your family responded.

c. Draw a picture to illustrate a verse about God's
   love or goodness. Some possible verses are Psalm
   16:11, Psalm 84:11, and John 3:16.

d. Plan a family visit to a hospital, a home for the
   elderly, or an orphanage. Before and after the
   trip, discuss how your family experiences God's
   blessings, and how you can share His goodness
   with others.

CHAPTER 3

IMITATING GOD'S CHARACTER

WHAT are the essential qualities of God's character? What is He like? Can we, in fact, imitate His character? Let us discover how definite—and encouraging—are the scriptural answers to these questions.

LIGHT AND LOVE

1. Read Exodus 20:1-17. What can you observe about God's character in the Ten Commandments?

   _____

   _____

   _____

   _____

2. How did Peter describe God in 1 Peter 1:15?

   _____

   What do you think it means to be holy?

   _____

   _____

   _____

3. Using Proverbs 6:16-19, list seven things which God hates and give an example of how each of them might occur in a family.

SEVEN THINGS	EXAMPLES IN A FAMILY SITUATION
(1) _____	_____
(2) _____	_____
(3) _____	_____
(4) _____	_____
(5) _____	_____
(6) _____	_____
(7) _____	_____

4. From Jeremiah 9:24, list the things in which God delights.

_____

_____

Give examples of how these can be practiced in a family.

_____

_____

_____

_____

5. Read 1 John 1:5 and 4:8. What two things did John say God is?

_____

_____

What do these two attributes mean to you?

_____

_____

_____

6. From the following passages, describe how God expresses His love, and use one word to sum up this particular character trait.

1 John 3:16 _____

_____

One-word summary: _____

Psalm 103:8-14 _____

_____

One-word summary: _____

John 13:3-5 _____

_____

One-word summary: _____

Philippians 2:5-8 _____

_____

One-word summary: _____

James 1:5,17 _____

_____

One-word summary: _____

"It is the nature of love that it cannot lie quiescent. It is active, creative, and benign. . . .The love of God is one of the great realities of the universe, a pillar upon which the hope of the world rests. But it is a personal, intimate thing, too. God does not love populations; He loves people. He loves not masses, but man. He loves us all with a mighty love that has no beginning and can have no end."

—A. W. Tozer*

"We need have no fear of Someone who loves us perfectly; His perfect love for us eliminates all dread of what He might do to us. If we are afraid, it is for fear of what He might do to us, and shows that we are not fully convinced that He really loves us" (1 John 4:18, *The Living Bible*).**

IMITATORS OF GOD

"Be imitators of God, therefore, as dearly loved children and live a life of love, just as Christ loved us and gave Himself up for us as a fragrant offering and sacrifice to God" (Ephesians 5:1-2).

7. Read Matthew 5:48. What did Jesus tell His disciples to be?

_____

*Tozer, *Knowledge of the Holy*, page 169.
**The Living Bible*, © 1971 by Tyndale House Publishers, Wheaton, Illinois.

What do you think this means?

_____

_____

8. Write John 13:34-35 here. (You may want to paraphrase it.)

_____

_____

_____

_____

9. Write a short statement about what you think it means for family members to love each other and their neighbors as Christ loved us.

_____

_____

_____

_____

10. What did Peter and John say in these passages about how Christians should live?

1 Peter 1:15-16 _____

_____

1 John 2:6 _____

_____

1 John 4:7 _____

_____

11. Read Mark 9:43-50. What do you think this passage means?

_____

_____

_____

12. Several specific guidelines regarding our overall conduct of life are given in Ephesians 4—5. Describe what the verses below say about our lifestyle, and add an explanation or practical example.

DESCRIPTION	EXPLANATION OR EXAMPLE
Ephesians 4:1	
Ephesians 4:15	
Ephesians 5:2	
Ephesians 5:8	
Ephesians 5:15	

13. From Romans 12:9-13, suggest some practical ways we can show love in our homes.

_____

_____

_____

_____

14. According to these verses, what has God provided
    so that we may live a godly life?

    2 Peter 1:3 _____

    _____

    Titus 2:11-12 _____

    _____

15. According to 2 Corinthians 3:18, what happens
    when we are exposed to the glory of the Lord?

    _____

    _____

    How can we expose ourselves to the Lord?

    _____

    _____

16. Read Galatians 5:16-18. Why is it difficult for
    Christians to live a godly life?

    _____

    _____

    What do you think it means to live by the Spirit?

    _____

    _____

    _____

17. The following passages include important steps to
    help you and your family in living godly lives.
    Match the statement with the verse.

a. Psalm 119:9-11   d. Matthew 26:41
b. Philippians 4:9   e. Colossians 3:5
c. Colossians 3:16   f. 2 Timothy 2:22

_____ Put to death worldly desires.

_____ Flee the evil desires of youth.

_____ Watch and pray.

_____ Let the Word dwell in you richly.

_____ Hide the Word in your heart.

_____ Put into practice godly things.

ENJOYING GOD'S CHARACTER

18. Read Galatians 5:22-23. What is the result of living by God's Spirit?

_____

_____

_____

19. From the principles given in these passages, what can result when we have Christian love and holiness in our homes?

John 17:20-21 _____

_____

_____

Matthew 5:16 _____

_____

APPLICATION

20. Based on what you have learned in this chapter, write a brief summary of what you believe are the most important attributes of God's character.

_____

_____

_____

_____

21. Select one or two passages from this chapter
    which particularly impressed you. List the
    references, and write down the thoughts which
    impressed you. Memorize one or both verses.

_____

_____

_____

_____

_____

_____

22. What are some important things that could be
    done in your home to stimulate one another to
    develop godly character?

_____

_____

_____

23. Prayerfully review your answers in this chapter.
    Briefly describe any need in your family or your
    own life that you believe you should work on at
    this time.

_____

_____

    What passage of Scripture brought this to your
    attention?

_____

_____

What specific action will you take to meet this need?

_____

_____

_____

How will you evaluate your progress?

_____

_____

_____

FAMILY PROJECTS

(Choose one or both.)

a. Read together the Beatitudes (Matthew 5:3-12). Find out what the word *blessed* means, and why these verses are known as "the Beatitudes."

Ask each family member to pick one of the verses and explain what the action or attitude mentioned in that verse means to him, and what it can mean in your home. Discuss also the promise mentioned for each characteristic. (You may want to have each family member dramatize a verse— perhaps in a charade, with others guessing what is being portrayed. Or try drawing illustrations depicting a beatitude.)

Ask each one to select a quality from the Beatitudes that he would like to see increased in his life, and to think of a way to develop it during the coming week.

b. Watch a television program or read a book together. Then discuss good and bad character traits you noted. Identify character traits which build up the family, and others which are destructive.

CHAPTER 4

LIVING UNDER GOD'S LEADERSHIP

HOW does God lead? How can we learn how trustworthy and loving His guidance is? God's leadership can be as exciting for our families as it was for the families of Israel traveling across the wilderness to Canaan. It was at this time that they sang, "In Your unfailing love You will lead the people You have redeemed" (Exodus 15:13).

HOW GOD LEADS

1. What aspect of God's presence with us is communicated in these passages?

Genesis 22:14 _____

_____

_____

Exodus 15:26 _____

_____

_____

Judges 6:24 _____

_____

_____

41

2. Read David's prayer of praise and thanksgiving in 1 Chronicles 29:10-19. From verses 11-16, list the truths you observe about God.

_____

_____

_____

_____

_____

_____

3. Record what the following passages teach us about God, and tell how these truths relate to your family.

TRUTH ABOUT GOD	RELATIONSHIP TO FAMILY

1 Chronicles 28:9

_____

_____

_____

Jeremiah 23:24

_____

_____

_____

Jeremiah 32:17

_____

_____

_____

_____

4. Using the truths about God from Questions 1-3, recall any personal experience you or your family have had which illustrated one of these truths.

_____

_____

_____

_____

_____

_____

5. God called David "a man after My own heart" (Acts 13:22). David was a man of outstanding achievements and admirable qualities, and despite some failures he maintained a strong, intimate relationship with God. God promised him that from his descendants would come the Messiah— certainly a supreme blessing and privilege for this man of God.

Study David's view of God in the verses below from Psalms. List the words David used to describe God, and tell what these words mean to you.

WORDS	WHAT THEY MEAN TO ME
Psalm 3:3	
Psalm 23:1	

43

Psalm 27:1

_____

_____

_____

Psalm 31:3

_____

_____

_____

GOD'S WILL

6. List the three ways Paul described the will of God in Romans 12:2; then write what these words mean to you.

GOD'S WILL IS . . .	WHAT IT MEANS TO ME

7. What can we learn about God's commands from 1 John 5:2-3?

_____

_____

_____

_____

8. List the main thought in the following verses.

Psalm 84:11 _____

_____

_____

Isaiah 40:11 _____

_____

_____

Romans 8:32 _____

_____

_____

Based on these verses, write a statement summarizing your conclusion about God's plan and desires for you and your family.

_____

_____

_____

_____

_____

_____

_____

_____

9. What did Isaiah write about following God's guidance in Isaiah 30:18?

_____

_____

_____

_____

_____

SUBMITTING
TO GOD'S
LEADERSHIP

10. In Romans 12:1-2, what did Paul say we should do
    to determine God's good, pleasing, and perfect
    will?

    _____

    _____

    _____

    _____

11. What decision of Joshua's is recorded in Joshua
    24:14-15?

    _____

    _____

    _____

    _____

12. From the following passages, briefly describe the
    circumstances involved and each person's attitude
    toward God's leadership. Then tell why you think
    this person may have demonstrated this attitude.

    Hebrews 11:8 (Abraham)

    Circumstances: _____

    _____

    _____

    Attitude: _____

    _____

    _____

    Possible explanation:_____

    _____

Hebrews 11:17-19 (Abraham)

Circumstances: _____

_____

_____

Attitude: _____

_____

_____

Possible explanation: _____

_____

Romans 4:18-21 (Abraham)

Circumstances: _____

_____

Attitude: _____

_____

_____

Possible explanation: _____

_____

Genesis 45:3-8 (Joseph)

Circumstances: _____

_____

_____

Attitude: _____

_____

_____

Possible explanation: _____

_____

Job 1:13-22 (Job)

Circumstances: _____

_____

_____

Attitude: _____

_____

_____

Possible explanation:_____

_____

_____

Luke 1:26-38 (Mary)

Circumstances: _____

_____

_____

Attitude: _____

_____

_____

Possible explanation:_____

_____

For each of these individuals, what were some of the results of submitting to God?

Abraham (Genesis 22:15-18)_____

_____

_____

Joseph (Genesis 50:20-21)_____

_____

_____

Job (Job 42:10-17)_____

_____

_____

Mary (Luke 1:46-49 and 2:16-20)_____

_____

_____

13. Draw a diagram in the space below showing relationships among God, husbands, wives, and children, and the order of submission taught in these passages: 1 Corinthians 11:3, and Ephesians 5:21-22 and 6:1-2.

DISCOVERING GOD'S LEADING

14. What did Paul write in Ephesians 5:17?

_____

_____

_____

_____

15. Read Proverbs 3:6. In what areas of our family life should we seek God's will?

_____

_____

_____

What does God promise us?

_____

_____

_____

16. Summarize the following passages.

Psalm 25:9,12 _____

_____

_____

2 Timothy 3:16-17 _____

_____

_____

Proverbs 15:22 _____

_____

James 1:5-6 _____

_____

_____

Psalm 66:18-19 _____

_____

_____

Isaiah 32:17_____

_____

_____

Proverbs 16:3_____

_____

_____

Hebrews 11:6_____

_____

_____

From these passages, make a list of steps for determining God's will.

_____

_____

_____

_____

_____

_____

_____

Here are a few questions by which to check yourself when determining God's leading:

1. What does the Bible teach about the area in which I am seeking guidance? (If there is no specific teaching, what scriptural principles apply?)
2. What is the counsel of godly people who know me? (This is necessary especially in major decisions, or when there is uncertainty about scriptural teaching, or if husband and wife disagree about what action to take. Remember also that counsel is not asking people to tell

51

you what to do, but obtaining more information in order to make your own decision.)
3. How has God led me in the past? What do I
know are His priorities for my life?
4. Are there other leaders or authorities I should
consult (such as a pastor or employer)?
5. What leadership responsibilities of my own
should be considered (such as family responsibilities)?
6. Have I surrendered my will to do whatever
God wants?

APPLICATION

17. Write a brief summary of the most important
truths you have learned in this chapter.

_____

_____

_____

_____

_____

18. Select one or two passages about God which particularly impressed you. List their references here,
and write down the thoughts from each passage
which impressed you. Then memorize one or both
verses.

_____

_____

_____

_____

_____

_____

_____

19. List any situations in which you and your family need to determine God's will at this time.

_____

_____

_____

_____

_____

_____

20. Prayerfully review your answers in this chapter. Is there any need in your life you should work on at this time? If so, briefly describe it.

_____

_____

_____

_____

What passage of Scripture brought this to your attention?

_____

_____

What specific action will you take to meet this need?

_____

_____

How will you evaluate your progress?

_____

_____

FAMILY PROJECTS

(Choose one or both.)

a. Read together Jeremiah 17:5-8 in a modern translation or paraphrase. Discuss with each other the two kinds of people this passage talks about. Then make a list of their characteristics—or draw illustrations of them—on a piece of paper or a chalkboard with two headings: "One who trusts in man" and "One who trusts in God."

b. Ask each person in your family to look for an example from your own lives or the lives of others; from the Bible; or from books, magazines, newspapers, or other sources, which shows a family or individual living under God's leadership. Then discuss what you've learned and how to apply that example to your family.

CHAPTER 5

INVESTING IN GOD'S KINGDOM

WHAT are we living for? God has provided in Scripture the guidelines for finding purpose and fulfillment in life. He gives us the privilege of spending our lives in a truly meaningful way.

GOD AND HIS KINGDOM

1. From Moses' prayer in Psalm 90:1-2, what can we learn about God?

   _____

   _____

   _____

2. Read Paul's charge to Timothy in 1 Timothy 6:13-16. Identify the titles and descriptions of God mentioned in verses 15-16, and explain what they mean to you. (Use a Bible dictionary if necessary.)

TITLES AND DESCRIPTIONS	MEANING

_____
_____
_____
_____
_____
_____

3. Read Isaiah 9:6-7. What did Isaiah foretell about the nature of the Lord's kingdom?

_____
_____
_____
_____

4. How is God's kingdom described in Psalm 145:13?

_____
_____
_____

5. Read Abraham's words to God in Genesis 18:25. What did Abraham call God?

_____

What confidence did he express in God?

_____
_____

What meaning does this have for you and your family today?

_____

_____

_____

_____

_____

_____

"In keeping with His promise," Peter wrote, "we are looking forward to a new heaven and a new earth, the home of righteousness" (2 Peter 3:13). God has planned His kingdom for eternity. How we respond to His plan will profoundly affect our temporal lives on earth. Knowing His purposes can give us hope and fulfillment.

INVESTING IN GOD'S KINGDOM

6. Read Matthew 6:19-34. What did Jesus say we should not do? (verse 19)

_____

_____

What do you think it means for a family to store up treasures on earth?

_____

_____

_____

_____

How do you think we can store up treasures in heaven?

57

_____

_____

_____

_____

_____

7. What promise from God do you find in Matthew
   6:33? What conditions are attached to the
   promise?

PROMISE	ANY CONDITIONS

What do you think it means to "seek first His
kingdom and His righteousness"?

_____

_____

_____

_____

_____

8. Rewrite Luke 9:24-26 in your own words.

_____

_____

_____

_____

_____

_____

_____

_____

_____

_____

_____

_____

_____

9. Read 1 Corinthians 3:11-15, then summarize
   Paul's teaching in verses 14-15.

_____

_____

_____

_____

10. What did Paul write in 2 Corinthians 5:10?

_____

_____

_____

11. After describing the destruction of the world,
    Peter told how Christians should live in light of
    these coming events (2 Peter 3:11-14). Summarize
    his teaching.

_____

_____

_____

THE KINGDOM
AND THE WORLD

12. The Bible uses the expression *the world* in different ways. Read the following passages and summarize what each one teaches about the world.

   Matthew 5:14 _____

   _____

   _____

   Mark 16:15 _____

   _____

   _____

   Romans 12:2 _____

   _____

   _____

   1 Corinthians 5:9-10 _____

   _____

   _____

13. In what ways is *the world* used differently in John 3:16 and 1 John 2:15-17?

   _____

   _____

   _____

   How should a Christian family relate to the world?

   _____

   _____

   _____

   _____

14. What do these passages tell us about the work God has for us today?

    Matthew 28:18-20 _____

    _____

    _____

    2 Corinthians 5:18-20 _____

    _____

    _____

15. How can Paul's statement in Colossians 1:28-29 be applied to the family?

    _____

    _____

    _____

    _____

    _____

    _____

SERVING IN GOD'S KINGDOM

16. From these passages, tell what was done to serve God.

    1 Samuel 1:27-28 _____

    _____

    _____

    John 12:1-3 _____

    _____

    _____

    _____

Acts 9:36 _____

_____

_____

Acts 18:27-28 _____

_____

_____

Romans 16:3-5 _____

_____

_____

Philemon 4-7 _____

_____

_____

17. Write Samuel's challenge to Israel in 1 Samuel 12:24 in your own words.

_____

_____

_____

_____

_____

18. What principles do you see in these passages about how we should regard our families as we serve in God's kingdom?

Matthew 10:37-38 _____

_____

_____

1 Timothy 5:8 _____

_____

_____

How should we combine these two principles in our lives?

_____

_____

_____

_____

_____

19. What things mentioned in these verses can keep our families from investing wholeheartedly in God's kingdom?

Mark 4:19 _____

_____

_____

Philippians 2:21 _____

_____

_____

2 Timothy 2:20-22 _____

_____

_____

2 Timothy 4:10 _____

_____

_____

APPLICATION

20. Based on what you have learned in this chapter, write a brief summary of what you believe are the most important truths about God's kingdom and its relevance to you.

_____

_____

_____

_____

_____

21. Select one or two passages about God and His kingdom which particularly impressed you. List their references, and write down the thoughts which impressed you. Then memorize one or both verses.

_____

_____

_____

_____

_____

_____

_____

22. In view of what you have studied, what are some practical steps your family can take to make sure you invest your lives in serving God's kingdom?

_____

_____

_____

_____

23. Prayerfully review your answers in this chapter. Is there any need in your life you should work on at this time? If so, briefly describe it.

_____

_____

_____

What passage of Scripture brought this to your
attention?

_____

_____

_____

What specific action will you take to meet this
need?

_____

_____

_____

How will you evaluate your progress?

_____

_____

FAMILY PROJECTS

(Choose one or more.)

a. Meditate on Matthew 6:33 by having different
   family members say the verse aloud, emphasizing
   a different word each time and thinking about
   what that emphasis communicates. (For example:
   "SEEK first His kingdom"; "Seek FIRST His
   kingdom"; "Seek first HIS kingdom"; and so on
   through the verse.) Or, sing the verse using a tune
   you already know or one you make up.

b. Identify a needy family in your neighborhood or
   church. Make a family project to serve them in a
   practical way.

65

c. Go through your house and garage and list items you seldom or never use—appliances, clothes, toys, or tools. Discuss what you could give to other families who could make better use of them. Consider setting aside part or all of your garden to give what you grow to needy families.

CHAPTER 6

CLAIMING GOD'S PROMISES

GOD'S promises are an endless source of treasure for a family living in close fellowship with Christ. "For no matter how many promises God has made, they are 'Yes' in Christ. And so through Him the 'Amen' is spoken by us to the glory of God" (2 Corinthians 1:20).

> "A promise is God's commitment to do something, and requires your response of faith in the form of obedience."
>
> —Walter A. Henrichsen*

GOD'S NATURE AND HIS PROMISES

1. What do you observe in these passages about the timelessness of the Lord's existence?

   Hebrews 13:8_____

   _____

   James 1:17_____

   _____

*Walter A. Henrichsen, *A Layman's Guide to Interpreting the Bible* (Nav-Press, 1978), page 44.

What assurance does this truth give you?

_____

_____

_____

2. What truth about God is revealed in Numbers 23:19?

_____

_____

3. Write out Nahum 1:7 in your own words.

_____

_____

_____

_____

4. The Book of Psalms is an excellent resource for learning about God. The writers of the Psalms communicate vital truths about God out of the vivid experiences of their lives. From the following verses, tell what truth about God is stated, and how this truth can relate to your family.

TRUTH ABOUT GOD	THIS TRUTH AS RELATED TO MY FAMILY
Psalm 46:1-2	
Psalm 57:10	

Psalm 68:19-20

_____

_____

_____

Psalm 86:5

_____

_____

_____

5. Read Deuteronomy 7:9. What did Moses teach the Israelites about God?

_____

_____

_____

6. Read Joshua 21:43-45. What was Israel's experience with God's promises?

_____

_____

_____

7. From the following passages, identify some facts about God's words.

Psalm 12:6 _____

_____

Psalm 111:7-8 _____

_____

_____

Psalm 119:89 _____

_____

Psalm 119:140 _____

_____

Proverbs 30:5 _____

_____

GOD'S PROMISES AND US

8. *Grace* is one of the most encouraging words in Scripture. Explain what it means to you; then use a Bible dictionary or concordance to expand your answer.

_____

_____

_____

_____

_____

_____

9. Read Ephesians 1:6-8. What does this passage say about God's grace?

_____

_____

10. What are some ways mentioned in these passages in which God has given us sufficient grace?

Romans 5:15-17 _____

_____

_____

2 Corinthians 12:9 _____

_____

_____

70

James 4:4-6 _____

_____

_____

11. From the verses below, list some of the purposes
for which God gave us His promises.

Romans 15:4 _____

_____

2 Peter 1:4 _____

_____

12. Make a list of the promises contained in the
following passages, and any related conditions.

PROMISE	CONDITION, IF ANY

Jeremiah 33:3

_____

_____

_____

Matthew 11:28-30

_____

_____

_____

John 15:5

_____

_____

_____

John 15:10-11

_____

_____

_____

71

Acts 1:4-8

_____

_____

_____

Philippians 4:19

_____

_____

Hebrews 13:5-6

_____

_____

_____

1 John 1:9

_____

_____

_____

"Let me tell you what I believe the need of the hour is. . . .I believe it is an army of soldiers, dedicated to Jesus Christ, who believe not only that He is God, but that He can fulfill every promise He has ever made, and that there isn't anything too hard for Him."

—Dawson Trotman*

CLAIMING GOD'S PROMISES

"The promises of God throughout the Bible are available to the Holy Spirit for the believers of every generation."

—Walter A. Henrichsen**

*Dawson Trotman, *The Need of the Hour* (The Navigators, 1957), page 10.
**Henrichsen, *Interpreting the Bible,* page 42.

13. What promises did these men claim and how did they claim them?

Solomon (1 Kings 8:25-26)_____

_____

_____

Nehemiah (Nehemiah 1:8-11)_____

_____

_____

_____

14. Read Psalm 51:4-13. How did David deal with his sin?

_____

_____

_____

15. From these passages in the Psalms, list some of David's basic convictions about God which sustained him in times of need:

31:14-15 _____

_____

56:3-4 _____

_____

130:3-4 _____

_____

138:8 _____

_____

16. What would you conclude from these verses about how you and your family can please God?

Psalm 147:11 _____

_____

Hebrews 11:6_____

_____

17. Tell how the examples or principles in the following passages can help us in claiming God's promises.

Psalm 119:49_____

_____

Philippians 4:6-7_____

_____

Hebrews 4:2_____

_____

_____

Hebrews 4:15-16_____

_____

_____

It is not enough to merely "have faith." The significance of faith is its object—the thing or person on which that faith is founded. Strong faith in an unworthy person or object is not commendable—in fact, it is foolish. But true Christian faith rests on the promises and character of God, as did the faith of Abraham—who was "fully persuaded that God had power to do what He had promised" (Romans 4:21).

18. Read Matthew 7:7-11. What assurance can your family have as you claim God's promises?

_____

_____

_____

19. From these passages, tell what can either help or hinder our experience of God's promises:

Psalm   106:10-12 _____

_____

_____

Psalm   106:13-15 _____

_____

_____

Psalm   106:24-27 _____

_____

_____

Hebrews 2:1 _____

_____

_____

Hebrews 3:12-13 _____

_____

_____

The results of giving glory to God in praise and gratitude are far different from the downward spiral of ingratitude.

INGRATITUDE

FORGETFULNESS

DISCOURAGEMENT

DOUBT

DESPAIR

GRATITUDE AND PRAISE

ENCOURAGEMENT

REMEMBRANCE

MORE FAITH IN GOD'S PROMISES

GOD'S ANSWERS

MORE PRAYER

20. How did Abraham respond to God's promise as recorded in Romans 4:20?

_____

_____

_____

APPLICATION

21. Write a brief summary of the most important things you have learned in this chapter about God and His promises to you and to your family.

_____

_____

_____

_____

_____

22. Select one or two passages from this chapter which particularly impressed you. List their references here, and write down the thoughts which impressed you. Memorize one or both verses.

_____

_____

_____

_____

_____

_____

23. Make a list of some needs or desires you or your family have. Find promises from God that are relevant to each need or desire, and list them also. Then claim these promises in prayer.

NEED OR DESIRE	PROMISE

24. Prayerfully review your answers in this chapter. Describe any need in your life you should work on at this time.

_____

_____

What passage of Scripture brought this to your attention?

_____

_____

What specific action will you take?

_____

_____

_____

How will you evaluate your progress?

_____

_____

FAMILY
PROJECTS

(Choose one or more.)

a. Discuss together what it is about God that enables Him to always keep His promises to us, while we are not always able to keep our promises to each other.

b. Let each person share a specific need or desire he has—something he would like God to do for him. Think about a scriptural promise that can be related to that need, and pray together, claiming the promise. (Review the list of promises in Question 12 to see if these might apply.)

c. Make a plaque or poster for your home to display a scriptural promise you are claiming as a family. Or, learn or make up together a song based on the promise.

THE BRIDGE ILLUSTRATION

To have a proper relationship with God and to obtain eternal life with Him, we must come to Him through Jesus Christ. This simple illustration of the Gospel can help you evaluate your relationship to God, or you can use it to help someone else receive eternal life.

The Bible teaches that God loves all men and wants them to know Him.

But man is separated from God and His love.

"God is on one side and all the people on the other side" (1 Timothy 2:5, *The Living Bible*).

Why is man separated from God and His love?

Because he has sinned against God.

"Your iniquities have separated you from your God" (Isaiah 59:2).

MAN   GOD

"All have sinned and fall short of the glory of God" (Romans 3:23).

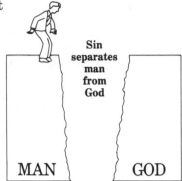

Where does this separation lead?

This separation leads only to death and certain judgment.

"Man is destined to die once, and after that to face judgment" (Hebrews 9:27).

"Those who do not know God . . .will be punished with everlasting destruction and shut out from the presence of the Lord" (2 Thessalonians 1:8-9).

But, there is a solution.

Jesus Christ, who died on the cross for our sins, is the way to God.

"God is on one side and all the people on the other side, and Christ Jesus, Himself man, is between them to bring them together, by giving His life for all mankind" (1 Timothy 2:5-6, *The Living Bible*).

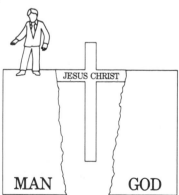

"Christ died for sins once for all. . .to bring you to God" (1 Peter 3:18).

Does this include everyone?

Yes. But only those who personally receive Jesus Christ into their lives, trusting Him to forgive their sins, can cross this bridge.

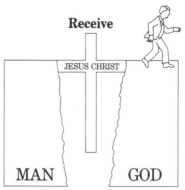

"To all who received Him, to those who believed in His name, He gave the right to become children of God" (John 1:12).

Everyone must decide individually whether to receive Christ.

Jesus says, "Here I am! I stand at the door and knock. If anyone hears My voice and opens the door, I will go in and eat with him, and he with Me" (Revelation 3:20).

How does a person receive Jesus Christ?

Jesus said, "You may ask Me for anything in My name, and I will do it" (John 14:14).

Therefore, if you pray sincerely, asking Him this:

Lord Jesus, please come into my life and be my Savior and Lord. Please forgive my sins, and give me the gift of eternal life.

—He will do it now.

If you have invited Jesus Christ into your life, the Bible says you now have eternal life.

"God has given us eternal life, and this life is in His Son. He who has the Son has life; he who does not have the Son of God does not have life" (1 John 5:11-12).

81

GUIDELINES FOR GROUP DISCUSSION

Discussing this book in a group—such as a Sunday school class or a Bible study group—will allow greater understanding of the scriptural principles you study. The format for this is simple: The group members first answer the questions to a chapter individually at home, and then discuss their findings with each other when they meet together, which is usually once a week.

If you are the discussion leader for such a group, the material on the following pages will help you guide the group in an edifying time of fellowship centered on God's Word.

BEFORE THE DISCUSSION

As the group leader, your most important preparation for each session is prayer. You will want to make your prayer requests personal, of course, but here are some suggestions:

• Pray that everyone in the group will complete the chapter preparation, and will attend this week's discussion. Ask God to allow each of them to feel the freedom to honestly share his thoughts, and to make a significant contribution to the discussion.

• Ask God to give each of you new understanding and practical applications from the Scriptures as you talk. Pray that the unique needs of each person will be met in this way.

• Pray that you, as the leader, will know the Holy Spirit's guidance in exercising patience, acceptance, sensitivity, and wisdom. Pray for an atmosphere of genuine love in the group, with each member being honestly open to learning and change.

• Pray that as a result of your study and discussion, all of you will obey the Lord more closely and will more clearly demonstrate Christ's presence in your families.

After prayer, the next most important aspect of your preparation is to be thoroughly familiar with the chapter you're discussing. Make sure you have answered all the questions and have read the leader's material for that chapter.

GETTING UNDER WAY

When your group is together, work toward having a relaxed and open atmosphere. This may not come quickly, so be especially friendly at first, and communicate to the group that all of you are learning together.

As the leader, take charge in an inoffensive way. The group is looking to you for leadership.

You may want to experiment with various methods for discussing the study material. One simple approach is to discuss it question by question. You can go around the group in order, with the first person giving his answer to Question 1 (followed by a little discussion), the second person answering Question 2, and so on. Or, anyone in the group could answer each question as you come to it (the leader saying something such as "Who would like to take Question 5 for us?"). The question-by-question approach can be a good way to get young Christians started in Bible study discussion. The obvious structure gives them a sense of confidence, and they can see where the discussion is going.

Another method is to lead with a section-by-section approach. This can provide more spontaneity. Start by asking the group for its impressions of the first section in the chapter you are studying (something like, "What impressed you most from this first section on prayer?"). Remember to direct your question to the entire group, rather than to a certain person.

Someone will then give an answer, probably by referring to a specific question in that section. You can have others share their answers, and then, to discuss the question more thoroughly, ask a good, thought-provoking question about this topic which you have made up beforehand. Later you'll begin this procedure again with the next section.

The key to a deeper, more interesting and helpful discussion is having good questions prepared. These should challenge the group to look more closely at the subject and Scripture passage you are discussing.

This leader's material includes suggested discussion questions for each chapter in this book. However, you will probably want to write some of your own as well, so make a list before each group meeting. Write as many as you can think of. Having a good supply to choose from will help you quickly launch the discussion, and keep it going in the right direction.

These guidelines will also help:

Asking questions
1. Make sure your questions are conversational.
2. Don't be afraid of silence after asking a question. Give everyone time to think.
3. Ask only one question at a time.
4. Don't ask questions which can be answered yes or no. This hinders discussion. Try beginning all your questions with "who," "what," "where," "when," "why," or "how."
5. A "What do you think?" question can help keep the discussion from seeming pressured or unnatural, since there is no such thing as a wrong answer to such a question. The person answering has freedom to simply give his viewpoint.

Other discussion
1. Remember that the Scriptures are the source of truth. Often you may want to look up together and

85

read aloud the verses listed for the study questions as you discuss your answers.
2. Summarize frequently. Help the group see the direction of the discussion.
3. Allow time for adequate discussion on the application questions in each chapter. Your goal in Bible study is not, of course, to have something to discuss, but to change your lives.
4. Allow adequate discussion also of the suggested family projects. Talk about how these can be adapted and implemented by everyone in the group.

General reminders
1. Your own attitude is a key factor in the group's enthusiasm. Develop a genuine interest in each person's remarks, and expect to learn from them.
2. Concentrate on developing acceptance and concern in the group. Avoid a businesslike or academic atmosphere.
3. Participate in the discussion as a member of the group. Don't be either a lecturer or a silent observer.
4. You may want to begin each session by reviewing memorized Scripture, and then discussing progress made in the previous week on applications and family projects.
5. Your total discussion time should probably not exceed ninety minutes, and one hour might be best. Start and end on time. Remember, too, to close in group prayer.

You'll want to review these lists often.

AFTER
THE DISCUSSION

Use these self-evaluation questions after each session to help you improve your leadership the next time:
1. Did you discuss the major points in the chapter?
2. Did you have enough prepared questions to properly guide the discussion?
3. Did you know your material thoroughly enough to have freedom in leading?

4. Did you keep the discussion from wandering?
5. Did everyone participate in the discussion?
6. Was the discussion practical?
7. Did you begin and end on time?

Chapter 1

UNDERSTANDING GOD'S CREATION

OVERVIEW	OBJECTIVE
a. Our Creator b. God's design in creation c. Seeing ourselves as God sees us d. God's design for the family e. Application f. Family projects	For each group member to understand more deeply how our Creator is the perfect, all-wise God who creates each individual for His glory, and who designed the family for our good.

For this session, and in later weeks, you may want to read the chapter objective and overview aloud to the group to help them see the overall focus of the chapter.

These questions from the study may promote the best discussion in your group as you share with each other your answers to them:

1, 3, 7, 8, 11, 12, 14, 17, 18, and 19.

Each chapter in the study material includes application questions. These are designed to help a person apply a biblical truth to his life in a practical way. Since the written answers for these questions are personal, group members need to have the freedom *not* to share their answers when you are discussing these questions. On the other hand, don't skip over the questions entirely, since the most beneficial discussion you can have is about how the Scriptures affect your day-to-day life.

87

A good way to stimulate discussion on an application question is to say something like, "Would any of you like to share with us your answers to Question 20?" or, "What did you learn about yourself (or your family) from Question 20?"

(In Chapter 1, Question 20 is an application question.)

Remember to discuss also the family projects. You may want someone to read aloud the instructions. Then discuss how the projects can be used and adapted in each family represented in your group.

FOR FURTHER DISCUSSION

These questions can help you stimulate further discussion on some of the questions in this chapter:

For *Question 1:* How should knowing that God is our Creator affect our attitudes and actions in these areas: marriage, friendships, career, and health?

Question 6 (Deuteronomy 32:4): Can we still say today that God's works are perfect?

Question 7: What does it mean to you personally that Christ is the head of the Church?

Question 11: What is a specific example of how we as human beings can glorify and honor God?

Question 13 (John 15:13-15): Do you think of yourself as one of Jesus' friends?

What can we do to deepen our friendship with the Lord Jesus Christ?

Question 14: How can we know that God desires unity in a family?

How can this influence the way our families live?

Question 15: Why do you think so much emphasis in these passages is placed on teaching God's commands to children?

When and where should children be taught the Bible?

Question 17: How would you summarize God's view of divorce?

88

Chapter 2

RESPONDING TO GOD'S LOVE

OVERVIEW	OBJECTIVE
a. What is God like? b. God loves us c. Responding to God's love d. Experiencing God's love e. Application f. Family projects	To understand how God is personal, loving, and knowable; and that He provided His Son, His Holy Spirit, and His Word to enable us to enjoy the privilege of a personal relationship with Him.

It will be important to refer to "The Bridge Illustration" on pages 79-82 if some of your group members need a clearer understanding of the Gospel.

You might also want various group members to read aloud and discuss point by point the information in the box following Question 18.

These questions from the study may promote the best discussion in your group:

1, 6, 10, 11, 15, 16, 18, 19, 20, and 21.

Questions 22 and 23 are application questions. Remember also to discuss the family projects.

It is often helpful to have someone read aloud a key passage pertaining to the chapter topic. A good passage for this chapter is Romans 8:31-39.

FOR FURTHER DISCUSSION

For *Question 2:* Which of these characteristics most impressed you?

Question 3: Why do you think Moses had such a close relationship with God?

Question 7: How can our families share the truth of this passage with other families?

Question 8: What is worship?
Question 11: How would you define sin?
Question 12 (Romans 6:23): Is eternal life entirely free?
Question 15: Do you think being born again can be a lengthy process?
Question 16: Why does the Lord command that we obey Him in order to experience His love?

Chapter 3

IMITATING GOD'S CHARACTER

OVERVIEW	OBJECTIVE
a. Light and love b. Imitators of God c. Enjoying God's character d. Application e. Family projects	To understand how God is holy and loving, and to be committed to live according to His standards.

These questions from the study may promote the best discussion in your group:

1, 2, 3, 4, 5, 7, 8, 9, 13, 16, 17, 20, and 21.

Remember also to discuss the application questions (22 and 23) and the family projects.

A good passage to have someone read aloud is Galatians 5:16-26 (or perhaps 1 Chronicles 29:10-19).

At one or two points in the discussion, you may find it appropriate to have a few moments of group prayer about a specific aspect of the study, such as character qualities of God we want to see developed in our lives.

FOR FURTHER DISCUSSION

For *Question 2:* Are there degrees of holiness?
Question 3: How can these be avoided?

Question 4: Which of these qualities is the easiest for you to understand and recognize?

Question 5: What is the relationship between light and love?

Question 10: How can we apply these extremely high standards to our lives?

Question 14: What confidence can we gain from the truths of these passages?

Question 16: Can you see this conflict going on in your children?

Question 18: Why do you think the word *fruit* is used to describe the results of the Holy Spirit's work in our lives?

Chapter 4

LIVING UNDER GOD'S LEADERSHIP

OVERVIEW	OBJECTIVE
a. How God leads b. God's will c. Submitting to God's leadership d. Discovering God's leading e. Application f. Family projects	To understand how God is our trustworthy Shepherd, Lord, and Leader, and has our best interests at heart; and to be convinced that the wisest course of action for our families is to trust and obey Him.

These questions may promote the best discussion in your group:

2, 3, 4, 6, 8, 12, 15, 16, 17, and 18.

Question 20 is an application question. Remember also to discuss the family projects.

You may want to read aloud and discuss point by point the material on God's guidance in the box following Question 16.

FOR FURTHER DISCUSSION

For *Question 5:* In what ways can we express our praise for God as David did in these psalms?

Question 6: How would this passage help when your family faces a major decision?

Question 7: Do God's commands ever seem burdensome to you? Why or why not?

Question 8: How have you recently seen God's goodness to your family?

Question 10: Do we have to offer our minds to God before they can be renewed?

Question 12: Which of these people—Abraham, Joseph, Job, or Mary—can you most readily identify with?

Question 15: How have you see this principle at work in your life in the past?

Chapter 5

INVESTING IN GOD'S KINGDOM

OVERVIEW	OBJECTIVE
a. God and His kingdom b. Investing in God's kingdom c. The kingdom and the world d. Serving in God's kingdom e. Application f. Family projects	To decide to invest our time and talents as a family in serving the kingdom of God; to understand the importance of living in the light of God's eternal values, and working for the advancement of Christ's kingdom on earth.

These questions may promote the best discussion in your group:

2, 5, 6, 8, 11, 13, 14, 15, 18, 19, 20, and 21.
Questions 22 and 23 are application questions.

FOR FURTHER DISCUSSION

For *Question 3:* Are these aspects of God's kingdom in evidence today?

Question 5: When do we need most to understand that God always does right?

Question 6: What are the differences between the kind of treasures we could store up on earth and the kind we could store up in heaven?

Question 8: How can we lose our life for Jesus Christ?

Question 9: What kinds of things in our life would survive this fire?

Question 11: How can children be taught to look forward to "a new heaven and a new earth"?

Question 14 (2 Corinthians 5:18-20): What is the work of an ambassador? What is the message that should be proclaimed by Christ's ambassadors?
Do you feel personally responsible for relaying to others God's message of salvation through Christ?

Question 17: What are the greatest things God has done for your family?

Question 18 (Matthew 10:37-38): How can we measure whether we love someone in our family more than we love the Lord?

Chapter 6

CLAIMING GOD'S PROMISES

OVERVIEW	OBJECTIVE
a. God's nature and His promises b. God's promises and us	To understand the value of God's promises, and how to claim them.

93

c. Claiming God's promises d. Application e. Family projects	

A good passage to have someone read aloud is Romans 4:18-24—a description of Abraham's example of faith, and what it means for us.

These questions may promote the best discussion in your group:

1, 3, 8, 10, 15, 16, 17, 18, 19, 20, 21, and 22.

Remember also to discuss the application questions (23 and 24) and the family projects.

FOR FURTHER DISCUSSION

For *Question 1:* How can the truths in these two passages affect your appreciation and understanding of the Scriptures?

Question 4 (Psalm 46:1-2): What things can make us fear?

What things can make our children fear?

How can they overcome these fears?

(Psalm 68:19-20): How have you seen God bear your burdens daily?

Question 6: Is this also true in your experience?

Question 9: How is it that God's grace comes to us through Christ?

Question 10: In what areas are you most aware of your need for God's grace?

Question 11: How can parents use scriptural promises to encourage and train their children?

Question 15 (Psalm 56:3-4): How do we overcome fear by trusting in God?

(Psalm 138:8): What other Scriptures do you know that tell us how God will fulfill His purposes for us?

Question 18: Why does God want us to pray about things?

SUGGESTED READING

Beers, V. Gilbert. *Family Bible Library*. Nashville: Southwestern Co., 1971.

Brandt, Henry R., and Dowdy, Homer E. *Building a Christian Home*. Wheaton, Illinois: Scripture Press, 1965.

Chafin, Kenneth. *Is There a Family in the House?* Waco, Texas: Word, Inc., 1978.

Christenson, Larry. *The Christian Family.* Minneapolis: Bethany Fellowship, 1970.

Hendricks, Howard. *Heaven Help the Home*. Scripture Press, 1974.

Henry, Joseph. *Fulfillment in Marriage*. Old Tappan, New Jersey: Fleming H. Revell, 1966.

Hunt, Gladys. *Focus on Family Life*. Grand Rapids, Michigan: Baker Book House, 1970.

Petersen, J. Allen, compiler. *The Marriage Affair.* Wheaton, Illinois: Tyndale House, 1971.

Rice, Shirley. *The Christian Home*. Fourth Edition. Norfolk: Tabernacle Church of Norfolk, 1969.

Schaeffer, Edith. *What Is a Family?* Old Tappan, New Jersey: Fleming H. Revell, 1975.

Small, Dwight H. *Design for Christian Marriage*. Old Tappan, New Jersey: Fleming H. Revell, 1971.

Tournier, Paul. *The Strong and the Weak.* Philadelphia: Westminster Press, 1963.

Williams, Norman V. *The Christian Home*. Chicago: Moody Press, 1952.